Disney
ELENA OF AVALOR

Look and Find

pi kids ® Phoenix International Publications, Inc.

Chicago · London · New York · Hamburg · Mexico City · Paris · Sydney

On her first day free from an evil magical spell, Elena, the soon-to-be Crown Princess of Avalor, meets her spirit animal Zuzo at the palace. Later, when shape-shifting "noblins" steal a royal ship with Elena's little sister Isabel on board, Zuzo reappears to help. He advises Elena to *listen* to the noblins' problem, and Elena learns an important lesson in ruling.

While Elena listens to Zuzo's advice, can you spot these troublesome noblins?

After a busy day, Elena officially becomes the Crown Princess! She appoints her Grand Council, choosing the four people who will help her be the best leader she can be.

Look for Elena's advisers and these royal accessories, fit for a princess:

Elena's grandmother

Esteban

scepter

crown

Naomi

Elena's grandfather

Though the duties of a Crown Princess are many, Elena promises to always be there for her sister Isabel. But ruling a kingdom can be tricky! Today, Elena is at the Invention Fair with Isabel, *and* she has some official dignitaries to meet at the same time.

Look around the Invention Fair and find these things while Elena tries to be in two places at once:

this tool

this invention

judge

Isabel's invention journal

this tool

Welcome Inventors

Elena appoints the young Mateo her new Royal Wizard, and right away she needs his help. When an evil wizard sneaks into the palace and turns everyone into stone, only Mateo can reverse the spell. Elena knows he can do it with his friends by his side!

As the magic begins to work, look around the royal throne room for these stone figures:

Mateo's mama

Armando

Elena's grandmother

Esteban

Elena's grandfather

Isabel

At the Día de los Muertos celebration, Elena and Isabel gather with family and friends to honor their parents and all those who have passed on to the spirit world. As Elena remembers her parents, she learns she has a new ability to see and speak to Ancestor Spirits! She uses her power to help a village family stop feuding.

As Elena and her friends celebrate, search the scene to find these Ancestor Spirits:

At her first Royal Retreat, Elena notices how the unkind King Hector bullies the other rulers. She decides to follow her own instincts. When a baby sea creature is in trouble, she rushes to help—and earns the respect of her new peers.

Find the baby sea creature and these nautical necessities:

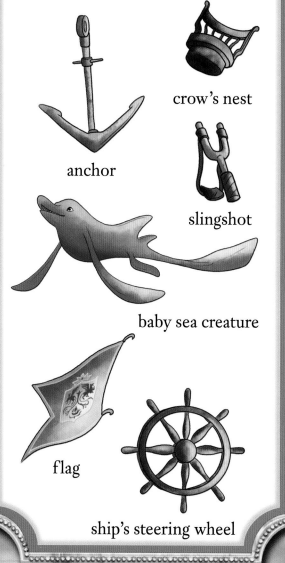

anchor

crow's nest

slingshot

baby sea creature

flag

ship's steering wheel

$\mathcal{A}$n ancient Maruvian chamber has been found underneath Avalor, and Elena puts Naomi in charge of the dig. When exploring the underground chamber, Esteban accidentally releases a *duende* that wants to cause chaos! Elena has to get to work sending the mischievous creatures back to their own magical realm.

Explore the underground chamber to find Elena, her friends, and these *duendes:*

Esteban

Elena

Naomi

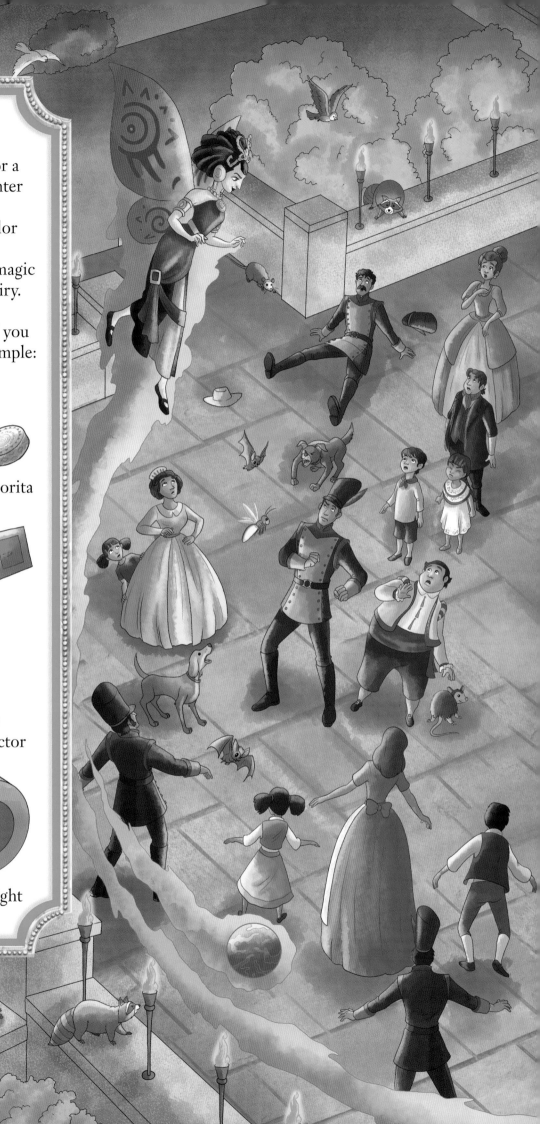

As Elena and Isabel wait for a rare solar eclipse, they encounter Orizaba the Moth Fairy and uncover her plan to send Avalor into eternal darkness! With Mateo's help, Elena uses her magic scepter to defeat the Moth Fairy.

Before the eclipse ends, see if you can find these things at the temple:

sun stone

Mateo's tamborita

this torch

Isabel's solar projector

Orizaba

Eye of Midnight

Hurry back to the ship to find Elena and her adventurous helpers:

Naomi

Zuzo

Elena

Isabel

Gabe

Skylar

Head back to Elena's coronation and find these things inside the castle:

royal portrait of Elena's grandfather

sash

this royal banner

Coronation of Princess Elena

royal portrait of Elena's parents

shield

this royal banner

Rush back to the Invention Fair and look for these important attendees:

this inventor

this dignitary

this dignitary

this inventor

this dignitary

this inventor

Go back to the throne room to find Mateo and these magical things:

spellbook

this statue turning back into human form

this statue turning back into human form

potion

Mateo

tamborita

Dance back to Día de los Muertos and spot these musical instruments:

maracas

drum

flute

tambourine

banjo

guitar

Sail back to the Royal Retreat and search for these rulers:

King Raja

King Hector

Elena

King Lars

King Joaquín

Shovel your way back to the archaeological dig and look for these tools:

hat

notebook

chisel

bucket

rope

brush

Sneak back to the Eclipse Festival and find these nocturnal animals:

this firefly

this owl

this bat

this opossum

this raccoon

this mouse